Native Americans

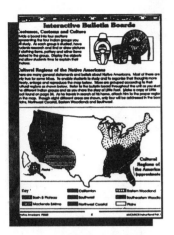

Teacher Resource Pages

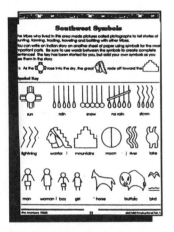

Student Activity Pages

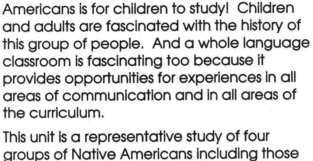

What an exciting theme unit Native Americans is for children to study! Children and adults are fascinated with the history of this group of people. And a whole language classroom is fascinating too because it provides opportunities for experiences in all areas of communication and in all areas of the curriculum.

This unit is a representative study of four groups of Native Americans including those from the Plains, the Northwest Coastal, the Southwest and the Eastern Woodlands. This material, combined with activities involving oral and written language, reading, poetry, vocabulary development, spelling, critical thinking, math, social studies, science, art and music, constitutes an exciting unit. Not only will your students enjoy it, but it will also serve to dispel many common stereotypes and misconceptions about Native Americans. How long you spend on the unit will depend upon the degree to which you extend the activities and the capabilities of your class. So have a "Heep-Waw" good time and enjoy this study of a truly fascinating people!

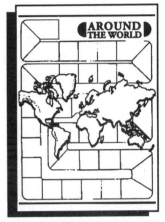

Full Color Gameboard

Award Certificate and Stationery

120 Reward Seals

An Original Story

A 6-foot Black and White Banner Which Reflects the Theme!

Setting the Stage

When you begin your Native American unit, make the entryway into your classroom into a wigwam, tepee or other type of Indian housing. (See pages 13, 22 and 35 for ideas.) Use newsprint around the door leading into your classroom to make it look as if students are stepping into an Indian shelter. Add various objects to your shelter to make it look more authentic (i.e. sticks at the top for a tepee). Have students research one of the four groups of Indians presented in this book and make symbols relating to the group they picked. Hang the symbols around the door after students have explained to the class what they stand for. *Suggestion: You might want to read all the way through the unit before you begin.

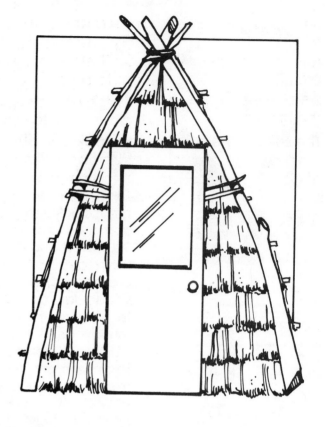

A Tribute to the Tribes Party

Celebrate the completion of the unit on Native Americans with a Tribute to the Tribes Party.

- Make invitations to invite parents, grandparents and administrators.
- Have a tribal feast. Serve corn bread muffins, dried beef jerky, nuts, berries, tortillas, cookies in the shape of tepees, etc.
- Share with the guests all the books, poems, art projects and science experiments that have been completed during the unit.
- You could also have the *Potlatch Party* at this time (page 28). People could draw numbers to exchange gifts.

The Parent Connection

Make copies of the letter on page 45 to send home to parents when you begin the unit. Sign and date it. If you need to add anything first, just write it inside the Indian shelter. Parent involvement is a great way to improve parent communication!

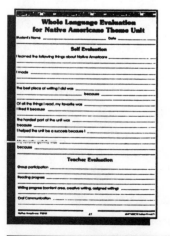

Evaluation of Students' Work

The unit evaluation can be developed in two ways. One is by assessing students on the basis of skills, knowledge, interest and behavior using the student projects as one criterion and observation of the students in class as the second criterion. These observations (anecdotal records) kept on each activity will give you information for a final evaluation. The second part of the unit evaluation will be completed by the students and you. At the end of the unit, guide the students through the Whole Language Evaluation on page 47 that asks the students to reflect on their study of Native Americans and allows you a place for evaluation also.

Creating the Environment

Setting up your classroom as a **Native American Community** will help unite your students as a "cooperative learning family" the second they walk in the door. To help your classroom reflect the Native American theme, make the *Interactive Bulletin Boards* on pages 4-6. Some of them you will want to prepare ahead of time such as "Cultural Regions of the Native Americans" on page 4. Others you will want to set up as the unit progresses or at the end of the unit.

The seals in the back of the book can be used on your classroom calendar (in place of the date) to help your classroom further reflect the Native American theme. For more information on the seals, see page 44.

Math and Science Center

This area can be as simple as a table set up for use for hands on math and science activities such as *The Eastern Woodland Hunters* (page 14), *The Southwest Weavers* (page 22) and *Light Line Graph* (page 32).

Creative Writing Center

Set up this area as a writing workshop as well as a place to display students' written work. Include all kinds of paper, *Native American Stationery* (page 48), markers, pencils, pens, cans of story starters, construction paper for book covers, stapler and tape. *Southwest Symbols* (page 23) and *Animal Lovers* (page 29) are just two of the many creative writing ideas mentioned in the book.

Reading Center

There is a wealth of books from your school library or public library about Native Americans, both fiction and nonfiction. *Literature Selections* are given on page 46. Encourage students to bring favorites from home, but make certain they are identified. Put class-made books in the center. Read to the students often.

Social Studies Center

This type of center will not be hard to establish, given the theme of this unit. For starters, set up the Interactive Bulletin Board "Native American Knowledge" (page 5). Students will have fun and learn a lot from this board. There are also many activity pages involving social studies in this book including *The Buffalo Hunters* (page 38).

On page 42 is an *Indian Chart* the students can use throughout their study of Native Americans. Have students fill it out as they learn new information about the Indian groups. It might also be fun for the students to have map puzzles of the U.S. depicting the four areas from which these Native Americans came.

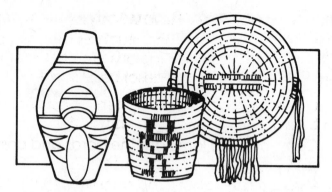

Interactive Bulletin Boards

Costumes, Customs and Culture

Divide a board into four sections representing the four Indian groups you will study. As each group is studied, have students research and find or draw pictures of clothing items, pottery and other items related to the group. Display the objects and allow students time to explain their choices.

Cultural Regions of the Native Americans

There are many general statements and beliefs about Native Americans. Most of these are only true for some tribes. To enable students to study and to organize their thoughts more clearly, enlarge and reproduce the map below. Tribes are grouped according to their cultural regions as shown below. Refer to the bulletin board throughout the unit as you study the different Indian groups and as you share the story of Little Foot. Make a copy of Little Foot found on page 34. As he travels in search of his home, attach him to the proper region on the map. Though eight different areas are shown, only four will be addressed in the book: Plains, Northwest Coastal, Eastern Woodlands and Southwest.

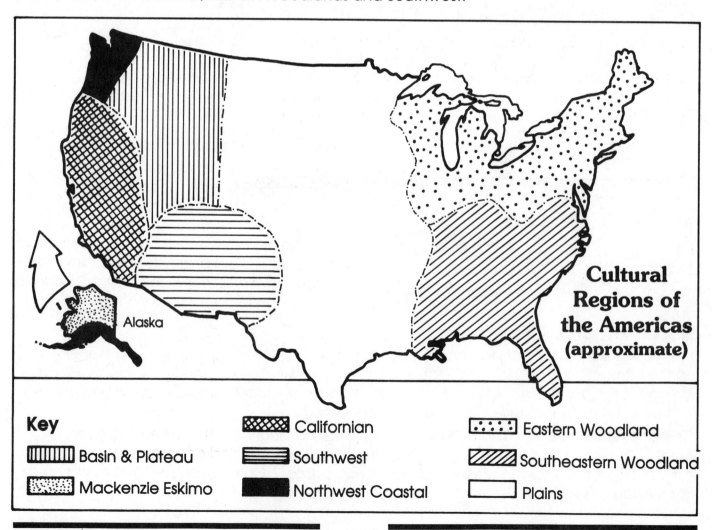

Cultural Regions of the Americas (approximate)

Key

▨ Californian	⬚ Eastern Woodland	
▥ Basin & Plateau	▤ Southwest	▨ Southeastern Woodland
⬚ Mackenzie Eskimo	■ Northwest Coastal	⬚ Plains

Interactive Bulletin Boards continued

Native American Knowledge

At the conclusion of the unit, students will have a clear idea of the culture and landscape of the four Native American regions. To encourage the application of this knowledge, use the interactive bulletin board described below.

1. Cover the board using students' beadwork from page 16 to create a border. Title the board, **Native American Knowledge**.
2. Copy, cut and laminate the cards and answer key on pages 7-8. (You may want students to color them first.)
3. Punch a hole on the top center of each card.
4. Use yarn to section the bulletin board into four parts and label as shown.
5. Place five straight pins in each section. Leave 1/2 inch of each pin sticking out.
6. Place the cards in a bag and hang them from the bottom of the bulletin board.
7. Fold the answer key in half and place it in the bag also.
8. Students place the cards in the appropriate sections of the board by using what they have learned in the unit. They can check themselves with the answer key.

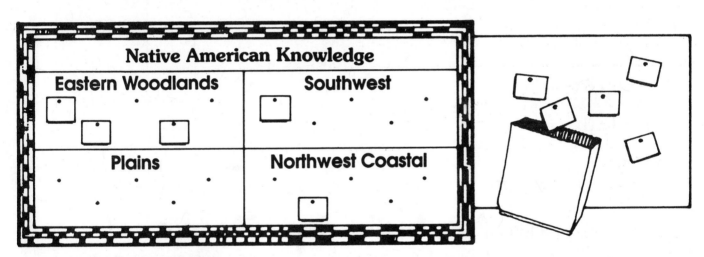

Native Comparisons

Do this bulletin board toward the end of the unit so students have enough information to use to make comparisons. Divide a bulletin board into five sections across and five down. Label the four Indian groups going across in the last four spaces. Label the following in the last four spaces going down on the left: **Food, Clothing, Shelter, Other**. Place students into four cooperative learning groups. Assign each group one of the four Indian groups. Have students find out what kind of food, clothing and shelter each group used. For the **Other** category, students can find characteristics or other interesting information relating to each Indian group.

Native Comparisons

	Eastern Woodlands	Plains	Southwest	Northwest Coastal
Food				
Clothing				
Shelter				
Other				

Interactive Bulletin Boards continued

Counting Coup

This bulletin board should be introduced during the study of the Plains Indians. Although the Plains tribes often took scalps of the enemy as a visual display, it was far more prestigious to "count coup." This meant earning and collecting honor feathers for acts of bravery like stealing a horse, striking an enemy with a bare hand or approaching an unaware buffalo.

Your class can "count coup" by earning feathers for team cooperation and responsibility. Use the bulletin board below to help you.

1. Make a chart similar to the one shown and attach it to a bulletin board.

2. As a class, decide the design for each type of feather and the behavior goals students will strive to achieve.

3. Have students use construction paper to design 6 feathers for each behavior (one for the key and five to earn).

4. You then award a feather when the class deserves one.

We're Counting Coup!					
= Good hallway manners					
= All homework turned in					
= All classwork finished					
= Desks cleaned					

5. When five of each of the feathers are earned, celebrate with a class party.

Making Individual Books

The original story, *Little Foot*, is divided into 4 sections. After each story section, there are sentence strips. (See page 11.) These strips should be used for making individual books of Little Foot's journey. (See directions below.) Students can either complete each section of the book after that part of the story is read or, they can save all the strips until the last section of the story is read.

1. Take the same number of pages of newsprint as there are sentence strips. Write 1 in the bottom right corner of the first page. Write 2 in the bottom right corner of the next page, etc.

2. Cut apart the sentence strips and lay them out in order.

3. Paste the first sentence at the bottom of page 1, etc. Illustrate each sentence.

4. After each section has been completed, use 2 more sheets of construction paper to make a front and back cover. Write the title and illustrate your cover.

5. Punch 3 holes down the left side of the book. Put brads in to hold the book together.

6

Cards for Native American Knowledge

Winter clothing:
buffalo hide coat

A favorite food:
buffalo liver

Skilled craft:
leather hides and
decorative feathers

Winter clothing:
parka made of fur

A favorite food:
raw fish

Skilled craft:
woodcarving

Winter clothing:
deerskin dress
with floral designs

A favorite food:
corn soup with fish

Skilled craft:
beadwork

Winter clothing:
cotton loincloth
and headband

A favorite food:
dried, crushed corn

Skilled craft:
weaving

More Cards for Native American Knowledge

Region includes:
Texas, Oklahoma, Kansas, Wyoming

Interesting fact:
The only tribes to wear feathered bonnets

Answer Key
Eastern Woodlands
1. deerskin dress with floral designs
2. corn soup with fish
3. beadwork
4. ME, NY, PA, OH
5. Ben Franklin used their ideas to form the U.S. government.

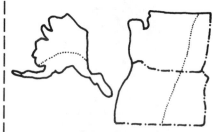

Region includes:
N. Oregon, S. Alaska, Washington State

Interesting fact:
After winning a battle, these tribes took heads rather than scalps!

Answer Key
Plains
1. buffalo hide coat
2. buffalo liver
3. leather hides and decorative feathers
4. TX, OK, KS, WY
5. wore feather war bonnets

Region includes:
Maine, New York, Pennsylvania, Ohio

Interesting fact:
Ben Franklin used their ideas to form U.S. government.

Answer Key
Southwest
1. cotton loincloth and headband
2. dried, crushed corn
3. weaving
4. southern UT, AZ, NM, northern Mexico
5. first tribe to get horses from Mexico

Region includes:
Southern Utah, Arizona, New Mexico, Northern Mexico

Interesting fact:
First tribes to get horses from Mexico

Answer Key
Northwest Coastal
1. parka made of fur
2. raw fish
3. woodcarving
4. N. Oregon, S. Alaska, Washington State
5. took heads of enemies after winning a battle

8

Activity of the Day

Use one of the activities below each day as an opening activity or during free time.

Write sentences about Native Americans beginning each line with one of the letters in the word INDIAN.	Most Plains tribes tested their boys for manhood. If they failed, they had to dress like a woman! Write a sentence telling how you feel about this.	The Indians are believed to have come from Asia over the Bering Straits into Alaska and then through the U.S. Draw a map of this.	Draw a Native American from one of the regions you are studying. Label the clothing and tell what it's made of.
The Woodland tribes grew 60 different types of beans! List and draw all the beans you can think of.	Which of the tribes would you like to have been a member of? Why?	Design a wordsearch for a friend. Use only Native American words.	Use an encyclopedia to list 10 Indian tribes of the U.S.
It is believed that only the Plains Indian chiefs wore war bonnets with trails of feathers. Draw one.	Instruments were important to all tribes. List the materials each region could have used to make drums, rattles and flutes.	Corn was an important food for the Woodland and Southwest tribes. Draw the life cycle of the corn from seed to full-grown plant.	Arrowheads have been found all over the U.S. Each is distinctive of its region. Research and draw four different arrowheads.
Use an encyclopedia to find the location of reservations today. Draw a map and include a key.	Imagine that you are an early American settler who stumbles onto an Indian village. What strange things do you see? Write about it.	Name four famous Native Americans.	The Native Americans cared deeply for the environment. Design a poster advertising good habits in caring for planet Earth.
There are many generalizations about Indians. Name three.	Many tribes painted their faces for war and religion. Design four ways to paint a face. Draw them.	Scramble ten words associated with this unit. Ask a friend to unscramble them.	The sun and the rain were important to all the tribes. List as many songs as you can think of that have "sun" or "rain" as part of the lyrics.

9

Beginning the Unit

- The best way to organize the unit is to do one Indian group each week. Begin each week with a part of the original story, *Lost Little Foot*.

- Explain to the children that you will be reading them a make-believe story about an Indian boy their age named Little Foot. He has lost his memory and can't remember where home is. Read them the first part of the story (page 11).

- Have the students create something for the "Costumes, Customs and Cultures" bulletin board (page 4) for each section.

- Show them the bulletin board entitled "Cultural Regions of the Native Americans." Locate the area Little Foot just visited. Ask students what states today are included in that area.

- Give students folders to keep their work in throughout the unit. Allow them time to decorate their folders to depict the unit of study.

- After each of the four story sections, give each student paper and the appropriate sentence strips to make his/her own Little Foot book. (See page 6.) They will keep the pages in their folders until their books are complete.

Little Foot and the Eastern Woodland Indians

- After reading your class the story, give them copies of the map and thermometers below. Talk about it together. Also give them the sentence strips so they can begin their books.

- Following the story are activities and teaching suggestions to help the students learn more about the Eastern Woodland Indians. At the same time, they will participate in activities that encompass the whole curriculum. They can be done in any order that suits the needs of your classroom.

- The *Language Development* (page 12) page includes creative writing and literature. These activities could be interspersed during the week spent on this Indian group.

- You might want to do *Shelter for the Eastern Woodland Indians* (page 13) early in the week so the students can have time to complete their longhouses or wigwams.

- Let students practice *The Hoop Dance* (page 17) during recess so they can present it at the party at the end of the unit.

Eastern Woodland Cultural Area

Below is a map of the area that was once the area of the Eastern Woodland tribes. Use the information from the map and thermometers to come up with logical answers to the questions below.

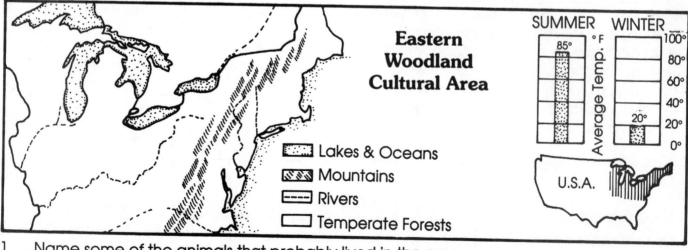

1. Name some of the animals that probably lived in the area. _____

_____

2. What did the tribes probably use for food? _____

   clothing? _____ shelter? _____

10

Lost Little Foot

An Original Story

Little Foot is lost! He had gone on his first buffalo hunt with his father, Chief Thunder Cloud, and some other Indian braves. He was so excited that somehow, he found himself separated from the group. To make matters worse, his pony threw him and he landed on his head. Little Foot couldn't remember what tribe he belongs to or how to get home!

So Little Foot climbed back on his pony and began looking for home. After several days, he saw an Indian village. The shelters looked like tepees. Then, he remembered, "I live in a tepee! Maybe this is my home!"

As Little Foot came upon the village, he began to look for his family's tepee. He met several Indian boys in deerskin leggings and shirts. He remembered that his friends at home wear this type of clothing too. He told the boys that he was lost and looking for his family's tepee. In a friendly way, the boys said, "Our shelters are called wigwams, not tepees. So this must not be your home. But we can offer you food and shelter."

Little Foot was starved and ate everything the boys' mother served him which included corn, beans and squash raised using the slash and burn method of farming. Soon he could not eat another bite, and he asked his new friends to tell about their people. He learned that they were Eastern Woodland Indians and that their people live in the area we know now reaches from the Canadian border south to the Gulf Coast and from the east coast west to the Mississippi River. They explained that their major tribes were the Chippewa, Delaware, Erie, Iroquois, Cherokee, Creek and Seminole Indians. Little Foot was fascinated by tales of their important ceremonial Green Corn Dance in which all wrongs are forgiven. Though Little Foot was having a great time, he knew he needed to continue his search for his own people. So, he thanked his friends and set out again on his pony.

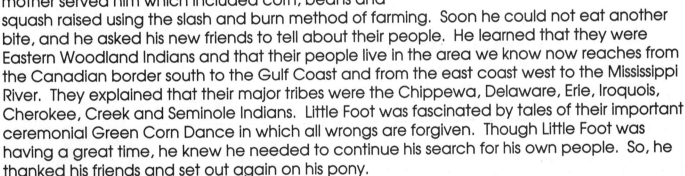

Little Foot went buffalo hunting one day with his father, Chief Thunder Cloud, and some other Indian braves.

The Green Corn Dance sounded fascinating to Little Foot, but he left to find his own family.

Little Foot's pony threw him causing him to bump his head and forget what kind of Indian he was or how to get home.

Little Foot first met a group of Eastern Woodland Indian boys who told him their homes were called wigwams, not tepees. They gave him corn, beans and squash to eat.

Language Development

Writing a Lesson

During the winter, many children of the Eastern Woodland Indians were taught manners and proper behavior by elder members of the tribe. The elders often told stories that would scare the children into behaving. Many of the stories included special gods or spirits including the two brothers Hawenneyu (Good) and Hanegoategeh (Evil). Other stories included the thunder god, Heno, who lived behind Niagara Falls.

Have students think about kindergartners and important lessons or behaviors they need to learn. Then, have them write a legend to teach the children the lesson or behavior. Have your students share their stories with the kindergarten class.

Legendary Literature

Many Woodland stories explained the existence of something, like *The Gift of the Sacred Dog* (Goble). This book tells the story of the gift of the horse to the Indians. Fill one corner of your classroom with folk tales from around the world. This exposure will help students develop a new style of writing while they enjoy these outlandish tales.

"Tracking" a Good Book

Many Eastern Woodland Indians hunted a great deal and were able to follow animal tracks in the snow or mud. To expose students to a variety of animal prints, make a class book! Each student chooses and researches an animal. Have the student use an index card to show the size and shape of the animal's paw print on one side. Students should be as accurate as possible.

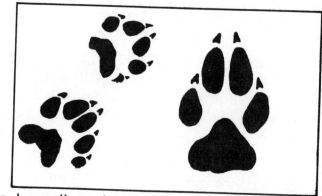

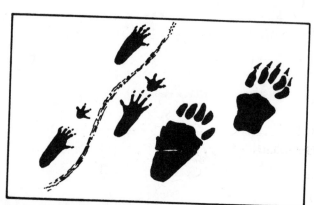

Then, have them tape the card (on one side only) onto a piece of construction paper. Under the card, have students draw a picture of the animal and its name. Have students make sure that the card hides the picture and the name of the animal. Collect the pages and bind them together. Display the book in the classroom and have students try to guess the prints. They can check their answers by lifting the cards.

Shelter for the Eastern Woodland Indians

The Iroquois, Mohicans and a few other tribes were hunters and farmers, so they lived together in an established community and moved only about every ten years. For this reason, their shelters were fairly permanent. They constructed long houses that were 25 -150 feet long, with 30-60 people living in each one. The materials included bark, branches, grass, evergreens and thatch. Each family was given an area 13 feet long and 6 feet wide with shelves as bunk beds. Down the middle of the house, fires burned for warmth and cooking, so the houses were usually very smoky.

Most of the other Eastern Woodland tribes were only hunters, so they moved often and needed shelter that could be taken down and reconstructed. They built single-family dwellings called wigwams using the same materials as the long houses. There were three types - domed (circular shaped), conical (cone-shaped) and wigwassawigamig (sloped sides). Each had a doorway and a smoke hole.

- Write the name of each house below.

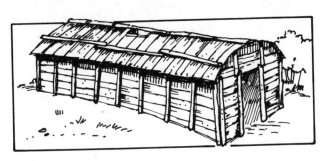

_____

_____

_____

_____

- Build a miniature long house or wigwam! Here's how:

1. With a partner, gather necessary materials (toothpicks, Popsicle™ sticks, grass, bark, branches, leaves, etc.).

2. Plan the frame of your shelter and use string, yarn or mud to hold it together. The Indians didn't use glue!

3. Add the walls and roof, but be sure to leave a doorway and smoke hole!

13

The Eastern Woodland Hunters

Although they did not eat only meat, hunting was of first importance to most Woodland Indians. The big season was from February until March.

The information below shows the game that was caught by two Eastern Woodland tribes. Use the information to complete a double bar graph comparing the successes of the two tribes. Be sure to use different colors for each tribe.

Iroquois Tribe

Mohawk Tribe

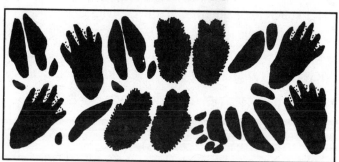

* Each print represents 4 animals caught.

Bear	
Beaver	
Deer	
Moose	
Rabbit	

0 2 4 6 8 10 12 14 16 18 20 22 24 26 28 30

☐ **Iroquois**   ☐ **Mohawk**

14

Canoe Construction

Because their region contained many rivers, lakes and streams, the Eastern Woodland Indians became expert craftsmen of the canoe. It was essential that the canoes be durable because they were used for hunting, travel, trade and in times of war. Canoes were constructed by a team of two men and four women, with the construction lasting from 10 to 21 days. The primary materials included wet, soft birch wood for the sides and bottom, spruce rootlets to sew the pieces together, boiled spruce gum to glue the pieces in place, and bark carved into "ribs" to support from the inside. The Indians had tried many different materials and processes before finding the one that worked out best. Now you can do the same using materials to build a small canoe that will float and hold pennies without sinking! Here's how:

1. With a partner, collect several types of materials that may be used to build an 8" canoe. Suggestions include: plastic containers, foil, plastic wrap, etc.
2. Begin construction of your canoe and document it on the chart below.
3. Test your canoe by placing it in a container of water. Then, slowly, add one penny to your canoe, then another, and another until your canoe starts to sink. Record the number of pennies.
4. Consider the cause of your boat sinking and change one thing about it (variable).
5. Repeat these steps three times, recording after each.
6. Complete the questions.

Try #	Describe the construction and any changes you made.	Draw your canoe and label the materials.	# of pennies	More or less than last try?	Reason for change

1. Which change was the most successful? Why? _____

_____

2. Name two important factors in building a canoe. #1 _____

   #2 _____

3. What do you think the Indians did to use those factors in building their canoes? _____

_____

15

Wampum Beadwork

The Eastern Woodland Indians had been using beads for decorations since before Columbus sailed to North America. They used seashells, bones, claws, stones and minerals to make beads. They were fortunate for their location along the coast, where quahog clam shells were common. These were used to make purple beads called wampum, and they were extremely valuable in trading. Using these beads, the tribes wove belts with floral designs or symbols of important events. You can create two Eastern Woodland designs below using different colors of pencils or markers. Be sure to use purple for the wampum!

*These can be used as a border for the bulletin board on page 5.

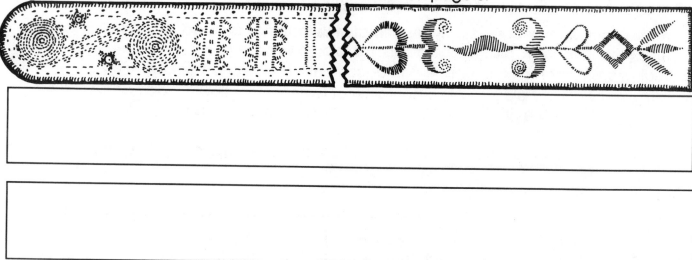

The False-Face Society

The Iroquois tribe of the Eastern Woodland Indians is famous for a special group of medicine men. These chosen few are said to have special healing powers when they put on their false faces, or frightening masks. Although the Iroquois carve theirs from wood, you can make a false face using the following materials:

12" x 18" colored sheet of construction paper, hole punch, pencils, crayons, string, various colors of tissue paper, yarn, construction paper, glue, scissors

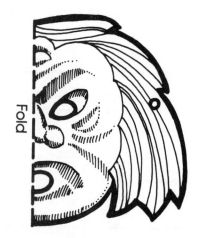

Fold

Directions:
1. Have your teacher enlarge the pattern. Then, cut it out.
2. Fold the 12" x 18" paper in half to make 12" x 9".
3. Lay the pattern on the folded paper, being careful to place the straight side on the fold.
4. Trace in pencil.
5. Cut along lines, but not the fold. Cut out the eye opening.
6. Hole punch on the side as shown on pattern.
7. Use tissue paper to decorate mask. Add details in crayon.

The Hoop Dance

Dramatic Expression/ Cooking

Because much of the northeast was once covered by trees, the Eastern Woodland Indians made good use of the wood, even in their dances. They often carved large hoops from soft wood, painted and decorated them, then practiced for months to master the dance.

You can also do the Hoop Dance using a hula-hoop from home. Decorate it with feathers and try these dance steps:

1. Hold the hoop in one hand and climb through it.
2. Swing it around your waist. Then, drop it down to your legs. Raise one foot and swing the hoop around it.
3. Put the hoop down, wiggle your toes under it to pick it up. Then, without your hands, wiggle it up your body.
4. Throw the hoop up and catch it in a variety of ways.

Now find a friend to play a drum as you practice in an Indian costume! The best dancers often did this dance with their hoop on fire!

Eastern Woodland Recipes

Because their meat supply depended on the success of a hunt, the Eastern Woodland Indians learned to grow and dry corn, beans and squash. Their natural sweetener was maple syrup, which they gathered and cooked in birch bark bowls.

Try these recipes using corn and squash!

Corn Bread Muffins

Ingredients: (for a group of 4)

1/2 c. flour	2 tsp. baking powder	1/2 c. milk
1/2 c. yellow cornmeal	1/4 tsp. salt	1/8 c. oil
1/8 c. sugar	1 egg	*baking cups

Directions: (Assign each student in a group a number from 1-4.)

Student #1	Measure, add and mix the flour and cornmeal.
Student #2	Measure, add and mix the sugar and baking powder.
Student #3	Measure, add and mix the salt and the egg.
Student #4	Measure, add and mix the milk and the oil.
Students #1-4	Spoon the batter into baking cups. Fill 1/2 way.
Teacher	Bake at 425° for 12-15 minutes or until slightly brown on top. Serve warm with butter.

Microwave Candied Squash

Ingredients: (for a group of 2)

1 small acorn squash	1/4 c. margarine	waxed paper
1/2 c. brown sugar	2 T. water	

Directions: (Assign each student in a group a name: Mohawk or Iroquois.)

Iroquois	Stab the squash with a fork in 10 places. Microwave on high for 8 minutes.
Mohawk	After 5 minutes, cut the squash crosswise into 7 or 8 pieces.
Iroquois	Gather seeds and discard. Place squash in dish.
Mohawk	Mix brown sugar, margarine and water.
Iroquois	Microwave mixture for 15 seconds. Stir and spoon over squash.
Mohawk	Cover with waxed paper and microwave for 3 minutes.

Little Foot and the Southwest Indians

- Explain to the children that you are going to share the next leg of Little Foot's journey in search of his lost family.
- After reading the story, remember to look at the bulletin board again and locate the area where Little Foot found the Southwest Indians. Talk about which states are included in that area today.
- After sharing the story, give the students the sentence strips on the bottom of page 19. You could allow them time to do their book pages now, or it could be an ongoing activity that could be worked on all week. At this time, give students copies of *The Southwest Tribes* mini-mapping activity (page 20). Encourage the students to add to their "maps" throughout the week.
- *The Apache Tus* (page 21) is a fascinating science activity for the students. *The Southwest Weavers* (page 22) challenges creativity and provides practice in geometry. *Sand Paintings* (page 21) and *The Cliff-Dwellers* (page 22) are fun art projects. Plus, they provide interesting information about the Southwest Indians.
- No Native American unit would be complete without rebus story writing. (See *Southwest Symbols*, page 23.) After the students have completed the activity, have them write another one on a brown paper bag torn in the shape of an animal skin.
- Southwest cooking has become popular all over the country. The foundation for many of the recipes found in restaurants today can be traced to the Indians. Several recipes are included on page 24. You might want your students to bring in some more to share. Perhaps you could make a class recipe book containing Native American recipes.

The Southwest Cultural Area

Below is a map of the area that was once the area of the Southwest Indian tribes. Use the information from the map and thermometers to come up with logical answers to the questions below.

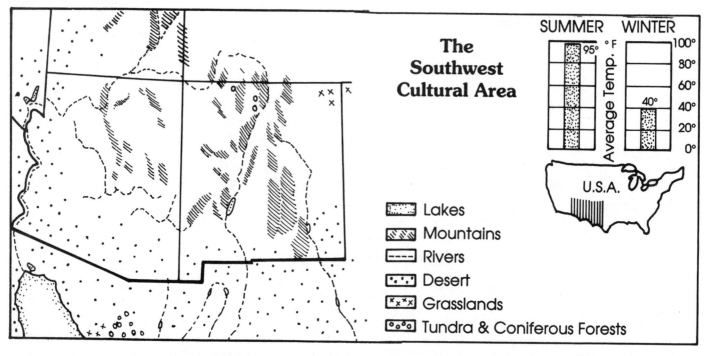

1. Name some animals that probably lived in the area. _____
2. What did the tribes probably use for food? _____
   clothing? _____ shelter? _____

Lost Little Foot - Part 2

Little Foot traveled for many days. Finally, he came upon another Indian village. "Is this home?" he wondered. As he drew closer, he saw large, many-storied dwellings. He knew the village was not his. He learned later that these dwellings were called pueblos. However, Little Foot was quite hungry - and thirsty too. The air seemed so dry! As he was sitting on his pony thinking about what to do, an Indian woman and her children walked up. Little Foot explained his dilemma, and she very kindly invited him for dinner and a night of sleep.

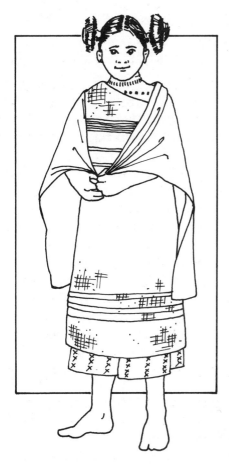

What a marvelous dinner Little Foot had! He had deer meat, corn, cactus fruit, roots and piñion nuts. Some of the foods he had never tasted, and he found them delicious! After eating, the Indians said a prayer to corn. That was something Little Foot had never heard before.

Though Little Foot was very tired, he wanted to hear what the kind Indian woman had to say about her people. He really hoped he was close to home. She told him they were Southwest Indians living in what is now Arizona, New Mexico, southern Utah and northern Mexico. "Our major tribes," she said, "include the Apache, Navajo, Pueblo, Taos Laguna Zuñi and Yuma Indians." Little Foot felt sad as none of these tribes sounded familiar.

But Little Foot listened with interest as the woman told about her people being famous for their bravery and fierce fighting. She related the story of Francisco Vasquéz de Coronado being the first European to meet her people. Little Foot was impressed with the handwoven blankets and sand paintings she had made. Before she knew it, the sad Indian boy was fast asleep.

The next Indians Little Foot came upon were the Southwest Indians.

They lived in large, many-storied dwellings called pueblos.

Here Little Foot had a wonderful dinner. He ate deer meat, corn, cactus fruit, roots and piñion nuts. After eating, they said a prayer to corn.

The kind Indian woman told Little Foot that the Apache, Navajo and Pueblo tribes among others were part of the Southwest Indians. She also told him they are famous for their bravery and fierce fighting.

Little Foot was impressed with the woman's handwoven blankets and beautiful sand paintings. But, he fell fast asleep!

The Southwest Tribes

Although these tribes shared an area of the United States and many of the same craft skills, they were completely different in one major way - their means of survival. For this reason, the tribes are divided into two groups: the Puebloan tribes who survived on their excellent farming skills, and the Athapaskan tribes whose existence depended primarily on raiding other villages.

During our study of the Southwest tribes, use the mind map below to help you distinguish between the two tribes. Whenever you learn something new, add it to the mind map.

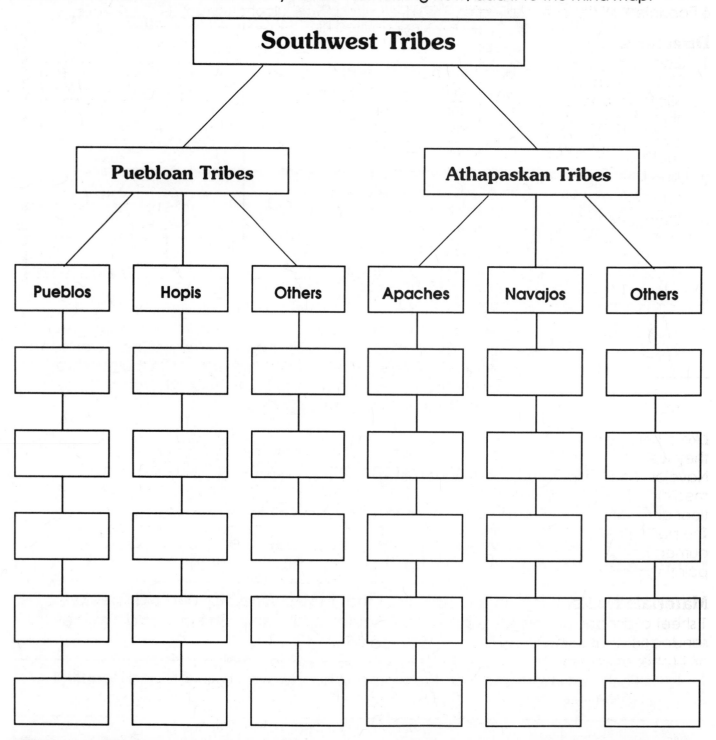

The Apache Tus

Although all of the Southwest tribes are excellent basketmakers, the Apache tribe of the Southwest is especially known for the tus, a water jug. This jug was considered special because it was tightly woven with many colors and then sealed with the sap of a piñion pine tree to make it waterproof.

Try the experiment below with your cooperative learning groups to see what else the Apaches could have lined the tus with to make it waterproof.

Materials Needed (per groups of 3 students)
6 Popsicle™ sticks, one cup water, 1 T. oil, glue, car wax, alcohol, syrup

Directions

1. Each group member should prepare two sticks by rubbing one of the substances all over them. (One stick will be rubbed with water.)

2. Set all the sticks in water for one minute.

3. On the chart shown, record your predictions of which sticks you believe will repel water.

4. Check each stick carefully. Record your observation on the chart.

Substance	Prediction		Observation	
	Repels Water	Absorbs Water	Repels Water	Absorbs Water
Oil (Indians gathered from nuts.)				
Glue (made from animals)				
Car wax (Indians got candle wax trading with white men.)				
Alcohol (also from trading)				
Syrup (from sap of trees)				
Plain wood				

Sand Paintings

Like other tribes, the Navajos believed that supernatural beings controlled their lives and that they were an important part of survival. When a member of the tribe became sick, the Navajos used an important ceremony called the healing sing. Just after sunrise, the medicine men would enter the hogan of the sick member. They would smooth the mud floor and paint a picture of the supernatural being who would be asked to cure the sick one. The person being treated would sit on the painting while the others sang, danced and burned herbs. Before morning, the paintings were destroyed. You can make a sand painting also!

Materials Needed
1 sheet of fine grain sandpaper and marker **or** 1 sheet of course sandpaper, tempera paints and brushes

Directions

1. Use an encyclopedia or other books to study the designs and colors used by the Navajos.

2. Plan your design in pencil.

3. Use the appropriate colors of makers or paints to complete the sand painting.

4. Display the paintings.

21

The Southwest Weavers

Because all of the Southwest tribes had access to cotton (from the crops) and wool (from herds of sheep), they became skilled weavers of blankets and rugs. With dye from berries and vegetables, the women created colorful designs in a variety of geometric lines and shapes.

Geometry

The Hopi rug below contains several equilateral, isosceles and scalene triangles. Use three crayons or markers to color the triangles according to the key shown.

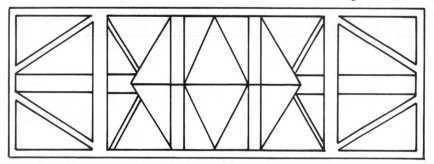

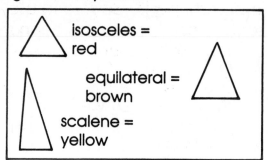

isosceles = red

equilateral = brown

scalene = yellow

Now create your own rug on the back of this paper. You must include: 5 equilateral, 4 isosceles and 3 scalene triangles.

The Cliff Dwellers

The people of the Southwest had very different dwellings than other Indians. Because the Hopis and Pueblos were farmers, they didn't move very often and lived in permanent villages. These were built on high plateaus of rock, called mesas. The villages were called pueblos and were made of adobe bricks. The walls were 7 feet high and very straight with small windows and no doors. The rooms were entered from ladders that led to holes in the ceilings. This was one form of protection from the raiding Apaches and Navajos. Each floor was set back by the depth of one room, and the very back rooms were used for food storage because they were cold and dark. Can you believe that the pueblos had no beds? It's a fact! You can make an adobe pueblo too!

Materials Needed

toothpicks or Popsicle™ sticks
construction paper scraps

brown paint
empty boxes

paintbrushes
scissors

Directions

1. Plan the layout of the pueblo and choose appropriate boxes for your design.

2. Cut small windows in the top of the boxes.

3. Tape the boxes together to form the shape and design of an adobe pueblo.

4. Paint the village brown.

5. Construct ladders from toothpicks or Popsicle™ sticks.

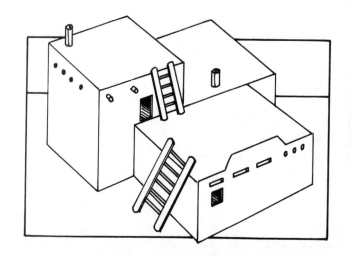

22

Name _____

Southwest Symbols

The tribes who lived in this area made pictures called pictographs to tell stories of hunting, farming, trading, traveling and battling with other tribes.

You can write an Indian story on another sheet of paper using symbols for the most important parts. Be sure to use words between the symbols to create complete sentences! The key has been started for you, but add your own symbols as you use them in the story.

Ex: As the ⊕ rose into the sky, the great 👤 rode off toward the ⬜

Symbol Key

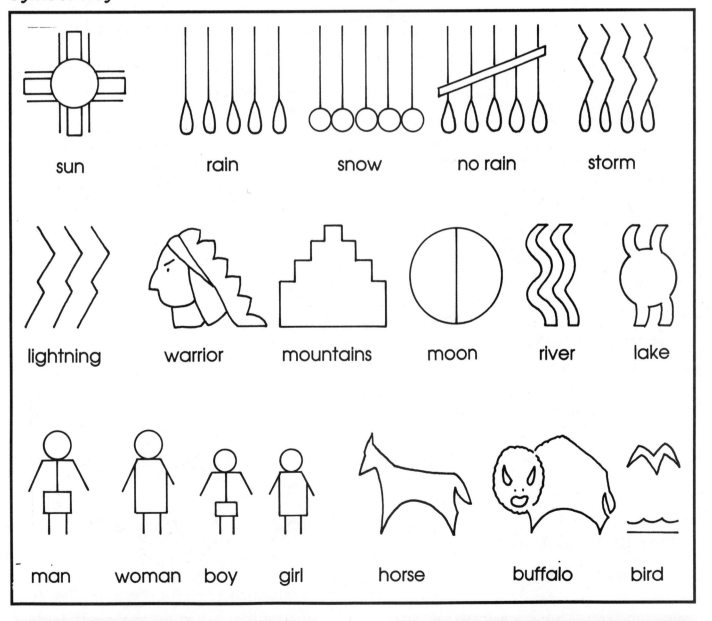

sun   rain   snow   no rain   storm

lightning   warrior   mountains   moon   river   lake

man   woman   boy   girl   horse   buffalo   bird

Southwest Cooking

The Indians of the Hopi, Pueblo and Zuñi tribes were well established farmers. This comes as a bit of a surprise because they lived in the desert! However, they learned that streams existed underground in the low areas and that some plants' roots could gather enough water to survive. They found that corn, beans, squash, tobacco and cotton grew very well when planted some distance apart. Because this was their main source of food, the Indians used these crops in nearly everything.

Try the recipe below using corn tortillas, a technique learned from the Mexicans.

Hopi Tortillas

Ingredients: (per pair of students)
2 corn tortillas   1/2 c. chili beans (canned) in their sauce
1/2 c. corn (canned)   1/4 c. cut green beans (canned)

Directions: (Assign each partner a number 1 or 2.)
Student #1   Measure the chili beans (and sauce). Put in bowl.
Student #2   Drain and measure the corn. Add to beans.
Student #1   Drain and measure green beans. Add to others.
Student #2   Mix well.
#1 and #2   Pour 1/2 of mixture over your tortilla. Enjoy!

The Southwest tribes were able to satisfy their sweet tooth at times also. The Hopi and Pueblo traded with other tribes to obtain maple sugar, while the Navajos and Apaches stole it during their raids. Try these recipes below to satisfy your sweet tooth!

Dessert (and Desert) Tortillas

Ingredients: (per student)
1 flour tortilla   1 T. butter or margarine   2 T. brown sugar

Directions: (Students work individually at group tables.)
1. Spread butter over tortillas.
2. Sprinkle sugar over butter.
3. Roll tortilla into a tube.
4. Microwave for 2-3 minutes on high.

Maple-Sugared Popcorn

Ingredients: (per 6 students)
1/3 c. unpopped corn   3 T. oil
1/3 c. brown sugar   1/4 c. water

Directions:
1. Combine unpopped corn and water. Set aside.
2. In 1 1/2 quart pan, heat oil. Add sugar.
3. Add popcorn and water. Cover.
4. Pop the corn quickly and shake the pan constantly.
5. After peak popping, remove from heat. Enjoy!

Little Foot and the Northwest Coastal Indians

- Again, tell the children that you are going to share the next leg of Little Foot's journey in search of his family.
- Remember to locate the area on the map where Little Foot found the Northwest Coastal Indians. Ask the children which states are included in that area today.
- After sharing the story, give the students the sentence strips on the bottom of page 26. Continue the process you began when the story was first introduced. At this time, give the students *The Storytelling Totem Pole* (page 27). Read the information together. Brainstorm some things they might put on their totem poles. Let this be an ongoing project for the week. As an alternative, you could have each cooperative learning group make one totem pole instead of individual ones.
- After their totem poles are finished, have a *Potlatch Party* (page 28). You will need to talk about the party at the beginning of the week so the children can be gathering gifts to bring. At the party, the children could share their original songs and poems (page 28).
- Children today are very aware of the problems of animals becoming extinct for a variety of reasons. Introduce *Animal Lovers* (page 29) by comparing the way Indians treated animals a long time ago to the ways they are treated today. Tie this into *The Makah and Nootka Whalers* activity (page 30).
- No study of the Northwest would be complete without an understanding of *The Midnight Sun* (page 31). Then, students can observe the amount of daylight they are having and how it changes (*Light Line Graph*, page 32).

The Northwest Coastal Cultural Area

Below is a map of the area that was once the area of the Northwest Coastal Indian tribes. Use the information from the map to come up with logical answers to the questions below.

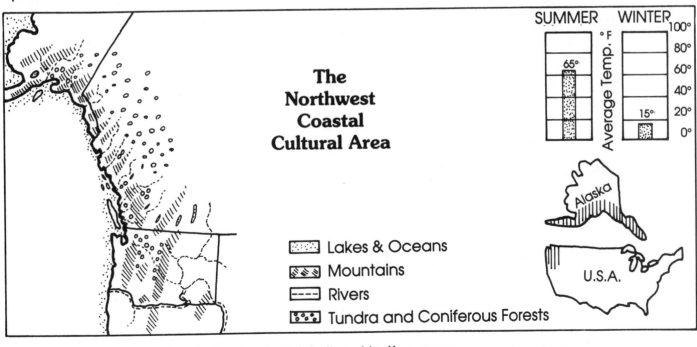

1. Name some animals that probably lived in the area. _____
2. What did the tribes probably use for food? _____
   clothing? _____   shelter? _____

Lost Little Foot - Part 3

The next day, Little Foot was on his way again looking for home. He decided to go to the ocean and then head up north along the coast because he remembered that his people like to fish. Sure enough, Little Foot stumbled onto a bunch of Indians fishing. They had many kinds of fish and other varieties of food from the sea. Little Foot watched as about 30 of them got into a canoe that looked as if it would hold 60 people and paddled away.

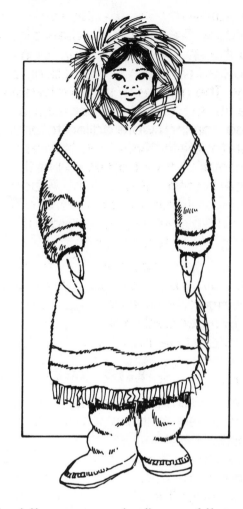

Little Foot was able to follow them on his pony to their village. But once there, Little Foot knew this was not home because all of them lived together in houses made with large beams and posts. There weren't any tepees to be seen! But Little Foot wanted to stop anyway as he was tired, hungry and discouraged.

This time, Little Foot met a pretty Indian girl who invited him to her house for lunch. Little Foot met many people at the girl's house because she lived with all her aunts, uncles and cousins. Little Foot was starved, but it took awhile before they could eat because they prayed to many gods first. They sat down to a lunch of seafood, bear, caribou, bulbs and berries. After lunch, Little Foot found out that these were Indians of the Northwest Coast and included the tribes of the Chinook, Bella Coola, Nootka and Haida among others. He concluded that these Indians make crafts from wood as he saw many decorative boxes, masks and utensils.

- -

Next, Little Foot met some Indians that rode in canoes that could hold up to 60 people and who made crafts from wood.

He followed the Indians to their village where he saw they lived in houses made with large beams and posts. There were no tepees to be seen!

Little Foot met an Indian girl who invited him to lunch. After praying to many gods, he ate seafood, bear, caribou, bulbs and berries.

Little Foot learned that the tribes of the Northwest Coastal Indians included the Chinook, Bella Coola, Nootka and Haida. But he still didn't know where he belonged. Little Foot felt sad and discouraged.

The Storytelling Totem Pole

Rebus Story

The Native Americans had several ways of remembering their heritage. Some of them drew pictures on rock walls which told the story of a great hunt or a fierce war. Others recorded events on animal skins, carefully painted to tell a story. The natives of the Northwest Coast carved large cedar tree trunks to tell the history of the family or an entire village. These carvings were called totem poles and were used as posts for the natives' long houses or as doorposts at the entrance to their homes. Sometimes they were simply placed in the middle of the village. The totem pole had carvings of animals, crests and other faces to tell a story. The natives were deeply religious and this was indicated through their totem poles.

A totem pole may have any number of figures on it. A family may have just one or several animal crests, which they see as their property. The crest may be the thunderbird, the bear or the two-headed serpent. Other common figures found on the totem pole include the whale, beaver, wolf, eagle and human figures. The order of the animals on the pole gives clues as to what the totem pole is trying to tell the viewer.

On the right is an example of some of the figures used on a totem pole. At the top of the pole is a thunderbird, possibly a family crest. The family may claim that the thunderbird came down, took off his animal clothing, and became one of their ancestors. Under the thunderbird is a killer whale, while under the whale is a bear. Beneath the bear is a raven, common to many totem poles and known as the trickster because of his stealing light from the darkness (thus playing bad tricks).

Make your own totem pole to tell your history or the history of your family. Think of symbols that you could include on your totem pole. For the first section (bottom) of your pole, draw a human figure, which would be you. On top of your picture, draw a symbol which would show what occupation one of your parents has. On the next panel, draw a favorite animal, which will be your family's crest. The next panel should include a symbol which shows what type of job you want to have when you grow up. Next, draw a symbol of something very important to you. You now have a personal totem pole.

Now, make your totem pole in a 3-dimensional form. You will need:

    cylindrical ice cream cartons with lids (obtain from an ice cream store), construction paper scraps, paintbrushes, yarn, ribbons, markers, scissors, crayons

To make the totem pole:

• Do some research on totem poles to find out what kind you want to make.
• Decide the story you want to tell and plan your totem pole accordingly.
• Use materials to decorate your ice cream cartons.
• Stack the cartons on top of each other to create the totem pole.

Potlatch Party

The tribes of this area became fairly wealthy as they had a constant supply of food and few worries about survival. Their wealth eventually made them self-centered, and they often displayed their riches (furs, totem poles, blankets) by having huge parties that lasted days or even months! During these celebrations, new totem poles were erected and wonderful gifts were given away. However, some potlatch parties became uncontrollable, with many of the rich forcing others to be their slaves and some even being killed.

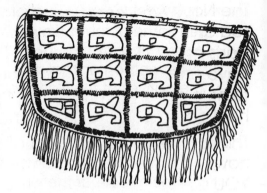

You can have a potlatch party when you erect your personal or group totem pole. Each person brings a handmade item to school to give away. Some ideas include:

a painting	a book for telephone numbers	a cupcake
a book	a tape-recorded song	craft items
a hair ribbon	flowers grown by you	a yarn necklace
a card	sports newspaper (written by you)	
a game	a decorated box for storage	

Poetry/Music

Poetry is an exciting way to tell a story. Listening to poetry, reading poetry and writing poetry are keys to helping students gain an appreciation for it. Set up a Poetry Corner. Make it an inviting, comfortable place. Place a tape recorder in it so students can both record and listen to poems. Include a collection of poetry books. Display class poetry on the wall with the caption: **CLASS POETS**

Acrostic Poems

Acrostic poems are fun to write. Here is a step-by-step approach to get students writing.

- Write TOTEM down the chalkboard.
- Brainstorm words that begin with each letter and list them.
- Brainstorm sample lines to make a poem.
- Have students choose an Indian noun and write their own poems.

T	- totem, to, try, today
O	- otter, often, on
T	- tell, telling, the
E	- each, every, end
M	- messenger, my, many

Totem poles
Often with the raven
Telling a story
Each one different
Messengers all

Writing Original Songs

Have the students write their own songs about Indians. They could make up their own tune or use familiar ones such as "One Little, Two Little, Three Little Indians," "Row, Row, Row Your Boat," etc. The whole room will be humming as the students work in their cooperative groups on this project.

Rappin' With the Natives

Students will have a blast with this! Have them create rap songs using information about Indians. Encourage them to be creative. Have them include facts in their songs.

Animal Lovers

Research/ Critical Thinking

The Northwest Coastal Indians relied heavily on land and sea animals as their food source, but they used all other parts of the animals as well. They believed that animals have an after life, in which they could return to Earth to help or hurt people, depending on how they had been treated. These Indians held ceremonies to thank animals. They never wasted any parts of animals.

This is not true, however, of all people who live in the Northwest Coastal region now. Many animals have been hunted so heavily that they now face extinction. YOU CAN HELP! Write a letter to the address below insisting that this stop. Then, ask your family and friends to write letters. The more letters they receive, the more seriously they will try to stop this before it is too late.

_____

The U.S. Fish and Wildlife Service
Office of Endangered Species
Washington, D.C. 20240

_____

_____

_____

_____

_____

_____

_____

_____

Research to find the names of specific animals that are near extinction.

How do you think the Indians that still exist feel about the near extinction of some animals? _____

_____

When is hunting necessary? _____

_____

When is it not? _____

_____

The Makah and Nootka Whalers

Research/ Analyzing

Although all the tribes of the Northwest Coastal area were thrilled to use whales as a source of food and supplies, only the Makah and Nootka tribes actually hunted them at sea. These Indians trained and purified themselves for three months before the hunt. Then, they set out in canoes. When a whale was spotted, the chief had the honor of striking with the first harpoon. Then, all others joined in until the whale was exhausted and eventually died. The Indians then tied the mouth shut so the whale's lungs couldn't fill with water and sink. The whale was then towed back to shore.

Imagine the difficulty of hunting an animal the size of a whale! To help you visualize this incredible feat, use encyclopedias to find the length of the whales listed below. Then, convert these lengths into feet and list a comparison to help you imagine the size.

Type of Whale	Length in Yards	Length in Feet	That's about as long as . . .
blue			
humpback			
killer			
sperm			

★ Fun Fact: An entire tribe could live a whole year on only 2-4 whales! ★

The Midnight Sun

Look closely at a map of the area covered by the Northwest Coastal tribes. Much of it is very close to the North Pole, which greatly affects their weather and length of daylight. Because Earth is tilted on its axis, this northern area has only a few hours of daylight in the winter. But in the summer, it is light through most of the night! The Itlinget tribe called this the Midnight Sun.

The length of your days change throughout the year also, but probably not so drastically. For the next two weeks, watch the news or read a newspaper to find the times of the sunrise and sunset in your area. Record them below. Then, find the length of each day's light.

Date	Sunrise	Sunset	Length of Daylight

Light Line Graph

**Math/
Graphing**

Use the data from the table on page 31 to create a line graph below.

How are the length of your days changing? _____

Predict the length of a day in two more weeks. _____

Why are these changes occurring? _____

When will they reverse? Why? _____

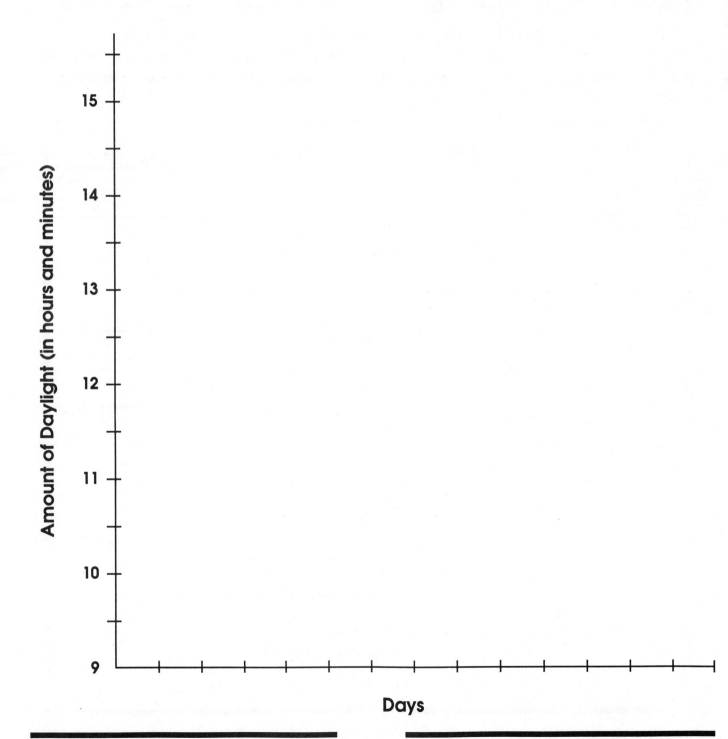

Days

(y-axis: Amount of Daylight (in hours and minutes), marked 9, 10, 11, 12, 13, 14, 15)

The End of Little Foot's Journey

- Explain to the children that you will finish reading the story of Little Foot's journey. Tell them that the story is open-ended. Talk about what that means. Ask the children what type of Indian Little Foot is (Plains). Have the children write a conclusion for the story.

- After reading the story, remember to look at the bulletin board and locate the area where Little Foot's people, the Plains Indians, live. Talk about the states included in that area.

- After sharing the story, give the students the last of the sentence strips on page 34. Have them complete their books. (See page 6.)

- *Magical War Shields* and *Plains Tepee* (page 35) are fun art activities for the students. While the students are working on the projects, have them imagine what it would be like to have to actually make a much larger version.

- *Inside a Tepee!* (page 37) and *The Buffalo Hunters* (page 38) require lots of thinking on the part of the students. After completing page 38, have the students tell why they chose a particular part for each item.

- *Dried Meat on the Plains* (page 39) is a great science activity. Remember to place the food in a place that won't be bothered by animals, other students, etc.

- *Sign Language* (page 40) is a great cooperative learning group activity. Try and use each group's sign as often as you can.

- -

The Plains Cultural Area

Below is a map of the area where the tribes of the Plains Indians once lived. Use the information from the map to come up with logical answers to the questions below.

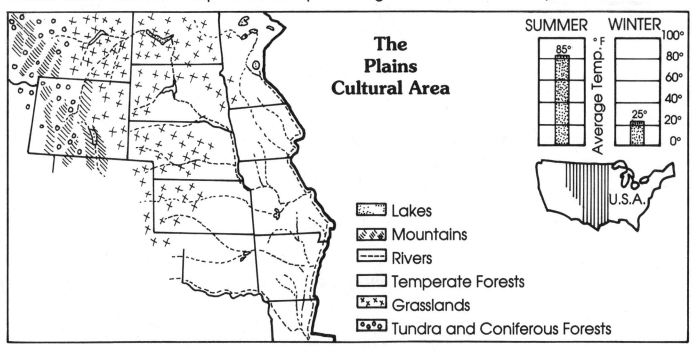

1. Name some animals that probably lived in the area. _____

2. What did the tribes probably use for food? _____

   clothing? _____   shelter? _____

Lost Little Foot - Part 4

Little Foot decided that before he left for another village, he had to figure out what Indian group he belonged to. His Indian friend suggested that he ask the wisest Indian of all - Chief Big Brain. So Little Foot climbed a tall mountain, went into a dark, scary cave and found Chief Big Brain smoking a peace pipe. Little Foot was surprised at the friendliness of this wrinkled, old Indian with long, white braids.

Little Foot told Chief Big Brain his predicament. The chief asked him to describe his people. Little Foot thought for a long time. Finally, he remembered a few things. He told Chief Big Brain that his people hunted buffalo during the summer, and that they put the slain ones on their travois and pulled them. He told the chief that he loved eating jerky his people made from the flesh of the buffalo.

Little Foot also remembered some of the major tribes of his group: Arapaho, Blackfeet, Cheyenne, Comanche, Crow, Osage and Sioux. Chief Big Brain asked him about fighting. Little Foot told him that next to buffalo hunting, warfare is his people's chief activity. Little Foot then explained counting coop to Chief Big Brain - a process in which an Indian earns feathers for bravery.

The wise old chief listened to every word Little Foot said. Then, he asked Little Foot to think really hard. Little Foot thought and thought. Yea! He remembered. Little Foot is a Plains Indian. He started his journey home by . . .

✂

Little Foot found the wisest Indian of all - Chief Big Brain. Hopefully, he could help him find his people.

Little Foot was able to tell Chief Big Brain about many tribes belonging to his group of Indians including the Arapaho, Cheyenne, Crow and Sioux.

Little Foot also told Chief Big Brain about counting coop.

Finally, Little Foot remembered what kind of Indian he was. He was a Plains Indian.

Magical War Shields

The Ojibwa tribe of the Plains used war shields for protection. These shields were made of buffalo leather that had been heated and shrunk for durability. The front was painted with symbols of enormous power that were seen as visions in magical dreams. The shield was so powerful that it was kept covered until an enemy approached. Then, it was uncovered to expose its full power. Make your own magical shield!

Materials Needed

1 heavy paper plate
crayons, markers or paint
18" strip of ribbon
craft feathers
ribbon scraps
glue
scissors

Directions

1. Decorate the bottom of the plate with symbols of power using markers, crayons or paint. (This is the front of the shield.)
2. Use scissors to cut slits on the sides for the ribbon to slip through.
3. Slip the ribbon through and tie it in knots to create a strap.
4. Glue decorative ribbons to your shield.

- -

Plains Tepee

When the herds of buffalo moved to new grazing areas, the tribes also moved to stay close to their food supply. This meant that the Plains Indians moved often and on short notice, which is why they lived in tepees. The small dwellings could be set up or taken down in about 10 minutes. They were each constructed of 16-20 poles and had a cover made from 20-30 buffalo hides. The small door always faced east toward the gods, and the two flaps of leather controlled the ventilation at the top of the tepee.

Materials Needed

8 1/2" x 11" piece of cloth or flattened paper bag   glue
5 pencils (6 1/2" long or longer)   crayons or markers   string

Directions

1. Cut out and trace the pattern from page 36 on the 8 1/2" x 11" piece of cloth or paper bag.
2. Decorate your tepee with Plains designs. Be sure to use the circular part as the bottom of the tepee.
3. Place 3 of the pencils in a tripod position with the erasers on the bottom.
4. Tie the tops together with string.
5. Wrap the cover around the pencils and glue the sides together. Be sure to leave the smoke flaps out.
6. Tie the tops of the smoke flaps to the 2 remaining pencils.

The Plains Tepee Pattern

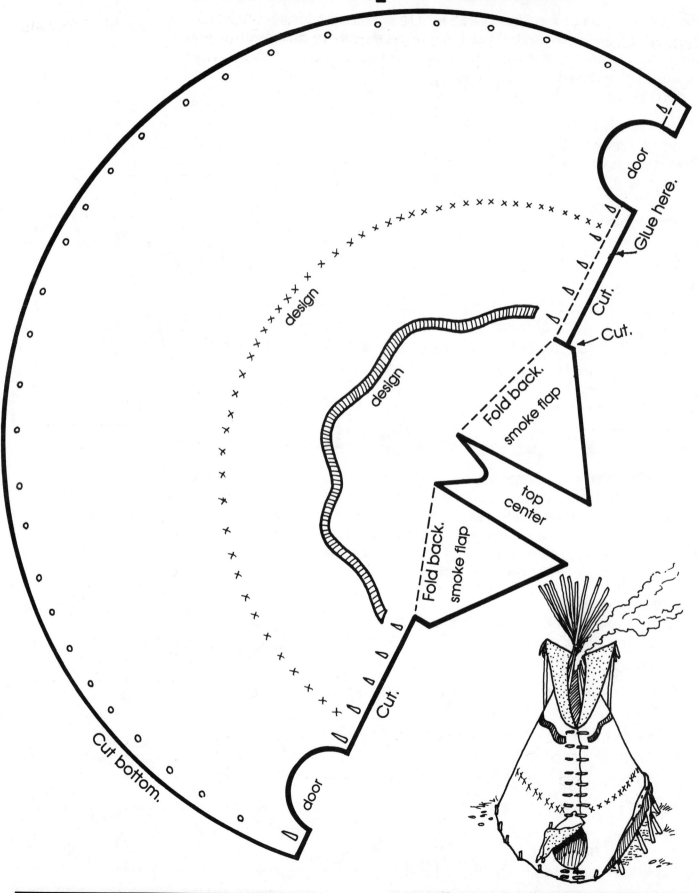

design

design

door

Glue here.

Cut.

Cut.

Fold back.

smoke flap

top
center

Fold back.

smoke flap

Cut.

door

Cut bottom.

Inside a Tepee!

Below are several items found inside a Dakota (Plains Indian) tepee. Cut out the pictures and then use the clues below to glue them in place where they belong in the tepee. Assume that you are in the center by the fire.

DOOR

Clues

1. The door is between the coup feathers and the buffalo head.
2. The buffalo head is to the right of the door.
3. The bed is next to the coup feathers.
4. The warrior's shield is to the left of the blanket.
5. The blanket is between the warrior's shield and the bed.
6. The bow and arrows are to the left of the warrior's shield and next to the scalp.
7. The scalp decoration and war bonnet are next to each other.

37

The Buffalo Hunters

**Logical Thinking/
Research**

The Plains Indians depended completely on the herds of buffalo for survival. They killed only as many as they needed and wasted none of the animal.

Below is a list of some buffalo body parts. Make a logical guess as to the function of each. Then, use an encyclopedia to find the actual uses. You may be very surprised!

Your Logical Guess		**Actual Use**
clothing, tepees, drums ●	● teeth ●	● clothing, tepees, drums
decorations ●	● brain ●	● decorations
bowls for cooking ●	● tongue ●	● bowls for cooking
cups, spoons ●	● hide ●	● cups, spoons
jewelry ●	● large intestine ●	● jewelry
strings on bows ●	● horns ●	● strings on bows
bags for storage ●	● muscles ●	● bags for storage
ropes, belts ●	● stomach ●	● ropes, belts
food ●	● hair ●	● food
tanning mixture for leather ●	● tail ●	● tanning mixture for leather

Now, fold your paper longwise down the center and hold it up to the light. The lines should match up if all your guesses were correct!

Name another body part and its function. _____

★ Fun Fact: The Plains Indians knew over 500 uses for the buffalo they killed. ★

Dried Meat on the Plains

Because the Plains Indians were never sure when the buffalo herds would move or become difficult to find, they were careful to save some meat from each hunt for later use. However, the meat would spoil quickly, so they learned to dry it in the sun and often crushed it into powder for preservation. In these forms, the meat would keep for years!

We still use this idea today! Below is a list of fresh and dried foods. Set a small portion of each in the sun for the experiment. Then, observe and record any changes.

Food	After 24 hours		After 48 hours	
	Draw	Describe using 5 senses	Draw	Describe using 5 senses
fresh beef				
dried beef jerky				
fresh milk				
dried powdered milk				
fresh fruit				
dried fruit				

Sign Language

Science

The many tribes of the Plains spoke several different languages and often could not understand one another. For this reason, sign language became their important means of communication. The gestures were easy to remember and could be learned quickly. Here are a few:

stream - right hand moves from right to left in a wave motion
rain - both hands held chest-high with dangling fingers
cry - same as rain, but hands held by eyes

Your students can make a class sign language! List some of the most commonly used words in your room on the chalkboard. Then, divide the class into six groups to make up gestures for each word. Let them take turns choosing words they want to do. Members of each group can then teach the rest of the class. Your sign language can now be used during lessons, assemblies, recess or any time to promote a quiet, yet productive classroom!

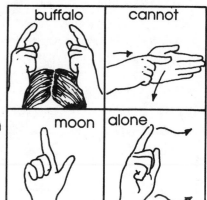

| buffalo | cannot |
| moon | alone |

Group One

word	gesture
1.	
2.	
3.	
4.	
5.	

Group Four

word	gesture
1.	
2.	
3.	
4.	
5.	

Group Two

word	gesture
1.	
2.	
3.	
4.	
5.	

Group Five

word	gesture
1.	
2.	
3.	
4.	
5.	

Group Three

word	gesture
1.	
2.	
3.	
4.	
5.	

Group Six

word	gesture
1.	
2.	
3.	
4.	
5.	

Decision-Making Map

As the United States government started forcing the Sioux off their land, they became irate and tried to keep their land by fighting back. They believed that the land belonged to them, and they were careful to take care of it. The white settlers believed that they were smarter and more deserving of the land. The two sides lost many men, women and children in the battles. Was there another way to solve the problem? Work with a partner to complete the chart below with the best solution.

Problem:	→	Goal:

Choices:	1.	2.	3.
Pros for each choice:			
Cons for each choice:			

Decision:	Reason:

41

Indian Chart

Fill out this chart throughout your study of Native Americans.

Indian Groups	Tribes	Types of Shelter	Food	Clothing	Unique Characteristics
Southwest					
Northwest Coastal					
Plains					
Eastern Woodlands					

42

The Native American Gameboard

Game Rules

Two to four students or groups of students may play at one time. There may be an assigned reader who reads the questions and checks the answers, or the players may read the questions to each other. If the question is answered correctly, the person or group answering correctly gets to move ahead one space. (Some of the harder questions may be given more value.) The students or groups keep taking turns until the first student or group reaches the United States. Use different-colored beans or chips as markers.

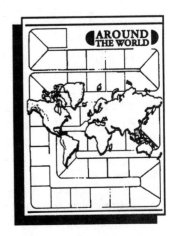

Answer Key

1. California, Basin, Plateau
2. wood, clay
3. tus
4. Plains
5. tepee
6. Answers will vary.
7. Northwest Coastal
8. Answers will vary.
9. Makah and Nootka
10. They were easy to take down and set up - great for tribes that moved a lot.
11. long house, wigwam
12. Answers will vary.
13. clothing, tepees, drums
14. Northwest Coastal
15. Plains

Game Cards

1. Name two cultural regions other than those we've studied.

2. Name two materials that Indians used to make dishes.

3. What is the Apache tribe especially known for that is also a water jug?

4. Which group of Indians relied primarily on buffalo hunting?

5. Name the type of shelters many of the Plains Indians lived in.

6. Name an untrue rumor about Indians.

7. Which group of Indians lived along the Pacific Ocean?

8. List four Indian tribes.

9. Which two Indian tribes of the Northwest Coast hunted whales at sea?

10. Why did many Indians live in tepees?

11. Name the types of shelters a Woodland Indian lived in.

12. Name a book about Native Americans and its author.

13. The Plains Indians made what from buffalo hide?

14. Which Indian group believed that animals have an afterlife?

15. Which group of Indians lived in the area that stretched from the Mississippi River to the Rocky Mountains?

Native American Seals

In the back of the book are 120 Reward Seals (6 each of 20 designs) consisting of 10 famous historic Native Americans and 10 famous contemporary Native Americans. (These famous people are listed below.) The seals may be used to reward students for reports on these Native Americans, to make flashcards or to create a gameboard. The seals are sold separately in packages of 60.

Historical Native Americans

Black Hawk (1767 - 1838) Sauk He was noted for his struggle against the westward movement of the white settlers in Illinois.

Tecumseh (1765? - 1813) Shawnee He was an outstanding leader of the eastern American Indian tribes after the American Revolutionary War.

Squanto (1585? - 1622) Patuxet He befriended the Pilgrims and helped them survive at Plymouth Colony. He served as interpreter between the colonists and the Wampanoag Indian chief and helped arrange a peace treaty.

Geronimo (1829 - 1909) Apache He was a warrior who led many attacks on troops and settlers in the Southwestern states and Mexico during the 1870's and 1880's.

Pocahontas (1595? - 1617) Algonquin She was the daughter of American Indian chief, Powhatan. It is claimed she saved the life of Captain John Smith, the leader of the settlers in Jamestown, Virginia.

Sitting Bull (1834? - 1890) Hunkpapa Sioux He was a famous medicine man and leader of the Hunkpapa Sioux Indians. He acted as the leading medicine man in the Battle of Little Bighorn.

Sacagawea (1787? -1812?) Shoshone She was a guide and interpreter for the Lewis and Clark expedition across western lands to the Pacific. She helped the party obtain food and horses from her relatives.

Sarah Winnemucca (1844? -1891) Paiute She won fame for her criticism of the government's mistreatment of her people. As early as 1870, she began speaking out against the government.

Crazy Horse (1844? -1877) Oglala Sioux He was a chief of his big tribe. He led the Indians in the Battle of Little Bighorn.

Chief Joseph (1840 ?-1904) Nez Percé He was a Nez Percé Indian chief who became famous for a retreat he led through Idaho and Montana in 1877.

Contemporary Native Americans

JoAllyn Archambault (1942 -) Sioux, Creek She is an anthropologist, college professor, artist and museum curator. Currently, she directs the American Indian Program at the Smithsonian Institution's Museum of Natural History.

Ben Nighthorse Campbell (1933 -) Northern Cheyenne He is a senator from Colorado. Elected in 1992, he is the first Native American in the U.S. Senate.

R. C. Gorman (1933 -) Navajo He is an energetic and prolific artist. He has been called "the Picasso of the American Indian artists." His paintings, pottery, weavings, masks, sculptures, etchings, silkscreens and lithographs are displayed in museums around the world.

Wilma Mankiller (1945 -) Cherokee She is the principal chief of the Cherokee Nation, the second largest Indian tribe in the country. She has brought nationwide attention to the plight of the American Indian.

Beatrice Medicine (1923 -) Hunkpapa (Lakota) In 1977, she was the Sacred Pipe Woman in the Sun Dance on the Standing Rock Reservation in North Dakota. Today, she in an anthropologist who teaches, writes professional papers and participates in important seminars on Native American matters.

N. Scott Momaday (1934 -) Kiowa In 1969, he was the first Native American to win the Pulitzer Prize for fiction for his book, *House Made of Dawn*. Currently, he teaches American Literature at the University of Arizona.

Orville Moody (1933 -) Choctaw He has played professional golf for over 20 years. Even though he only won the U.S. Open during his career with the Professional Golf Association tour, he has won many tournaments on the senior tour.

Jim Thorpe (1887 - 1953) Sac and Fox He is called the "greatest American Athlete of the first half of the 20th century." In the 1912 Summer Olympics, he won gold medals for the pentathlon and the decathlon.

Mervin Ringlero (1917 -) Pima, Papago and Cahwilla He is one of the last great saddle makers in the country. Many actors and stuntmen who appeared in Western movies rode saddles made by him. His saddles became famous for their beautiful designs, durability and comfort.

Susan Laflesche Picotte (1865 - 1915) Omaha She was the first American Indian woman to become a physician. She earned her M.D. degree in 1889 from the Women's Medical College of Pennsylvania. After getting her degree, she worked to improve medical care on the Omaha reservation in northern Nebraska.

Date _____

Dear Parents,

Today was the first day of our theme unit about Native Americans. We are all excited about the fun we are going to have learning across the curriculum with Native Americans as our theme. Each day, ask your student what went on at school. Emphasize questions about Native Americans such as:

- Can you name some Indian groups?
- Can you name any specific tribes?
- What kinds of foods did these particular Indians eat?
- What types of shelters did the Native Americans live in?
- What customs make these people unique?
- Have you read a special book about Native Americans? Tell me the story.

We are creating a Native Americans environment in our classroom. We are studying the Plains Indians, the Southwest Indians, Indians from the Northwest Coast and the Eastern Woodland Indians. If you have any objects relating to these groups of Native Americans, or to Indians in general, we would appreciate your lending them to us. We will take very good care of them. Books and recordings related to Native Americans would also help us with our study. Please identify them so they can be returned to the right person.

Also, if you can help with any of the projects below, please check and return the form.

Thank you for your continued support.

_____
teacher

- -

I can do one or more of the following:

☐ Read a book about Native Americans to the class

☐ Bake tepee-shaped cookies for the Tribute to the Tribes Party

☐ Other _____

☐ Help with food at the Tribute to the Tribes Party

☐ Bring books or other objects related to Native Americans

_____
signed

_____
date

Literature Selections

Bernstein, M. and Kobrin, J. *Earth Namer: A Californian Indian Myth.* New York: Charles Scribner's Sons.

Clark, A. *The Desert People.* New York: The Viking Press.

Field, E. *Eskimo Songs and Stories.*

Gobel, P. (1984). *The Gift of the Sacred Dog.* New York: Macmillan Child Group.

Gorsline, D. and Gorsline M. (1978). *North American Indians.* New York: Random Books Young Reader.

Henry, E. 1983. *Native American Cookbook.* New York: Julian Mersner.

McDermott, G. (1974). *Arrow to the Sun: A Pueblo Indian Tale.* Viking Press. (Caldecott winner)

Pine, T. *The Indians Knew.* New York: McGraw Hill.

Stuart, G. (1974). *Three Little Indians.* Washington, D.C.: National Geographic.

Tamarin, A. *We Have Not Vanished.* Chicago: Follett Publishing Co.

Below are series that are suggested for use:

Indians of North America. 63 volumes. (1987). New York: Chelsea House Publishers.

Indian Tribes of America. Florida: Rourke Publications, Inc.
>   *Sioux.*
>   *Seminole.*
>   *Cherokee.*
>   *Iroquois.*
>   *Navajo.*
>   *Ojibwe.*

A New True Book. Chicago: Children's Press.
>   Lepthien, E. (1985). *Cherokee.*
>   Lepthien, E. (1985). *Seminole.*
>   Martini, T. (1982). *Indians.*
>   McKissack, P. (1984). *Apache.*
>   Osinski, A. (1984). *Sioux.*

Native American People. (1989). Florida: Rourke Publications, Inc.
>   Brooks, B. *Seminole.*
>   Brooks, B. *Sioux.*
>   McCall, B. *Cherokee.*
>   McCall, B. *Iroquois.*
>   Stan, S. *Navajo.*
>   Stan, S. *Ojibwe.*

Whole Language Evaluation
for Native Americans Theme Unit

Student's Name _____ Date _____

Self Evaluation

I learned the following things about Native Americans _____
_____
_____

I made _____
_____
_____

The best piece of writing I did was _____
_____ because _____
_____

Of all the things I read, my favorite was _____
I liked it because _____
_____

The hardest part of the unit was _____
because _____
I helped the unit be a success because I _____
_____

My favorite activity was _____
because _____

Teacher Evaluation

Group participation _____
_____

Reading progress _____
_____

Writing progress (content area, creative writing, assigned writing) _____
_____

Oral Communication _____
_____

_____

_____

_____

_____

_____

_____

_____

_____

_____

_____

_____

_____

_____

earned the

Native American Award!

For _____

_____

_____   _____
teacher   date